Eyes & Ears 2

The next step

A method for the development of sight-reading skills
through aural and visual awareness by means of duet playing

James Rae

www.**universaledition**.com

vienna · london · new york

UE 21 142

ISMN: M-008-06676-4
UPC 8-03452-01408-9
ISBN 3-7024-1682-X

Eyes and Ears

Eyes These are the first means of contact a musician has with a new piece. They relay all the musical data from the page to the brain which then decodes this information and tells the musician what to play. The speed at which all this happens depends on how often the player reads music. Similar to reading words, the more you read, the more fluent you become.

Ears As well as our two physical ears, we also have a third 'ear' in our brain which enables us to 'hear' music without it having been played. Composers and musicians, particularly in the field of jazz, have highly developed 'inner ears' which enables them to write down or play the music they hear in their minds. This facility is also of great importance to instrumentalists as it allows them to hear a piece of music by just looking at it. Unfortunately, most people are not born with this skill but it can be acquired by regular sight-reading practice.

Acquiring both keen EYES and EARS is the key to successful sight-reading and this facility is one of the most valuable assets any musician could wish to possess.

Certain skills can be practised by yourself, but similar to playing tennis or chess, you make the most progress when you play with a person of a higher standard. By doing this you are immediately put 'on the spot' and will have to keep going, even at the risk of making the odd mistake. Through good positive duet playing, fluency and confidence in sight-reading will develop. You will learn to play exactly what you see, and not what you think you see and through the development of a strong sense of pulse, musical notation will no longer appear as a jumble of strange, irrelevant symbols.

The *Eyes and Ears* series from Foundation Level to Advanced will provide a wealth of material with which to acquire a good sight-reading facility. It is not essential however to have worked through the series from Level 1 to gain benefit. Most players will find an appropriate book in the series suitable to their needs but bear in mind it is not always a bad thing to go back to basics and consolidate skills.

James Rae

Confidence

Confidence is probably the most important and yet the most misunderstood aspect of playing any musical instrument. It plays an essential part in the art of sight-reading. I have seen this word written so many times on exam report sheets. e.g. *'a little more **confidence** would greatly improve the performance'*. **But**, what this really means is *'a lot more **practice** would greatly improve the performance'*.

Confidence comes from *security*. Security comes from *familiarity* and familiarity, no matter how you look at it, comes from ***regular practice***.

In the case of sight-reading, you are expected to play an unfamiliar piece of music as if you know it well. Being confronted with a new piece can be compared, psychologically, with walking into a room full of strangers. In this situation you naturally feel on-edge and behave differently from how you would if the room was full of your best friends. In order to feel confident in the company of strangers, you must put yourself in this situation on a regular basis and after a while it will become a less daunting and more enjoyable experience. The same applies to sight-reading. It is probably the most feared part of any practical music examination, but with regular practice it can actually be fun! As with all other aspects of playing, sight-reading does improve with practice.

Five Golden Rules

Always look at the first 10cm of the music

Learn to absorb key signature, time signature, speed indication (tempo) and dynamics.
(*p, mp, mf, f* etc.)

Scan the whole piece

Take note of any changes of dynamics, awkward rhythms and tricky technical passages.

Select a pulse

You must have a solid pulse (beat) in you mind in order to sight-read accurately.

Once you have started, don't stop!

This is very important especially when playing with other musicians. They should not be expected to stop just for your benefit. Once the train is in motion, you cannot jump off!

Always look ahead

Don't look at the notes you are playing, look at those you are about to play. It is similar to driving a car. You don't look at the road immediately in front of the bonnet as it will be very quickly behind you! Look well ahead in order to react to the vast amount of information coming at you.

Contents

The Up-beat

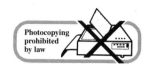

The Up-beat is a note or a group of notes which appears before the first complete bar of a musical phrase. It is also known as an *anacrusis* or *pick-up*. Many melodies begin with an up-beat.

Please note that the last bar of a piece beginning with an up-beat will often be shortened by the value of that up-beat. e.g. If a piece of music is in $\frac{4}{4}$ time and it has an up-beat of **one crotchet**, the last bar will only be **three** beats long.

a) Exercises with crotchet up-beats

TOP TIP *Always have a solid pulse in your head before commencing to play.*

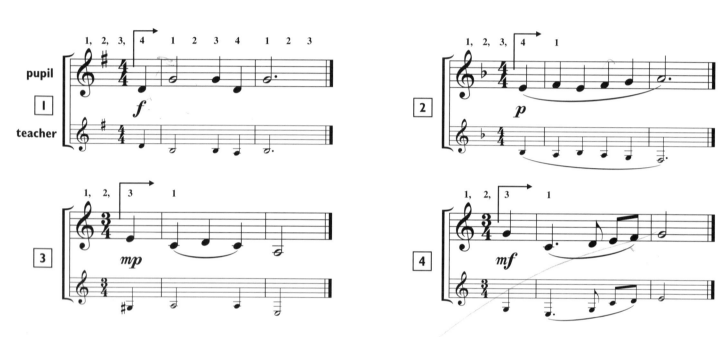

Putting it Together ❶

UE 21 142 L

b) Exercises with single quaver up-beats

Putting it Together ❷

c) Exercises with two quaver up-beats

Putting it Together ③

d) Exercises with three quaver up-beats (♪♫)

This is one of the most common types of up-beats. It is also one of the most difficult to grasp as it starts on an 'AND'. i.e.

♪ ♫ |

and four and   *etc.*

TOP TIP *Always give yourself a good strong mental count-in.*

Putting it Together ④

 **TOP TIP** *Don't be distracted by 'clashes' in the harmony. Remember, ALWAYS play EXACTLY what you see.*

Semiquavers

In simple time, i.e. **2/4**, **3/4** or **4/4**, semiquavers are usually grouped in two or fours (♫ or ♬♬).

They are often 'beamed' together with quavers, i.e. ♪♫ or ♬♪ . A good way to feel semiquavers is to

think:- ♪♪♪♪ as you play.
ONE, AN, AND, A

TOP TIP *Do not confuse semiquavers with quavers. There are **four** per crotchet beat.*

Putting it Together ⑤

UE 21 142 L

TOP TIP *Don't play semiquavers too fast especially in slow moving pieces.*

a) The dotted quaver/semiquaver rhythm

This is another example of a rhythm which is often misread.

TOP TIP *Play the semiquaver as late as possible. It is rhythmically a 'lead in' to the next strong beat.*

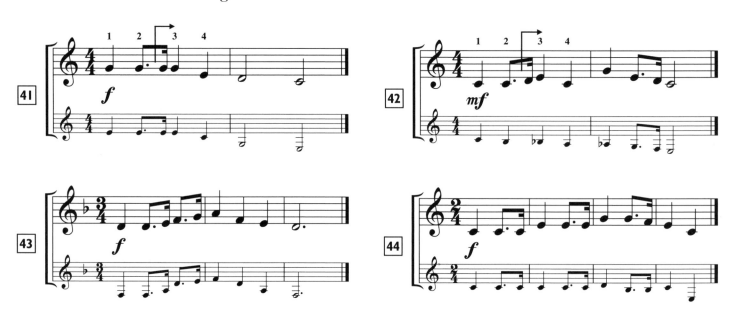

Putting it Together ⑥

TOP TIP *Don't confuse dotted rhythms ♪. ♪ with even quavers ♪♪*

16

The following exercises use the dotted quaver/semiquaver rhythm as an up-beat.

Syncopation

Up till now we have dealt with melodies where the main notes fall 'on the beat'. In syncopated music, some important notes are placed 'off the beat'. These notes are commonly known as 'off-beats'. They are usually placed after a quaver or quaver rest and cut across the pulse of the music.

 **TOP TIP** *In order to play syncopated passages accurately, it is essential to have a strong regular pulse in your head so that you can 'bounce off' the on-beats in the music.*

* = Off-beat

Putting it Together 7

The $\frac{3}{8}$ Time Signature

In a slow tempo $\frac{3}{8}$ will have three quaver beats per bar and in a fast tempo it will only have one dotted crotchet beat (divided into 3.)

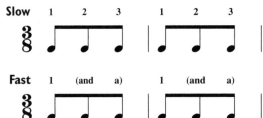

TOP TIP ♪. ♪♪ *is very common in* **3/8** *and* **6/8** *time. Think of the word* Wim-ble-don *to feel the rhythm correctly. (Like* ♩. ♪♪ *in* **3/4** *.)*

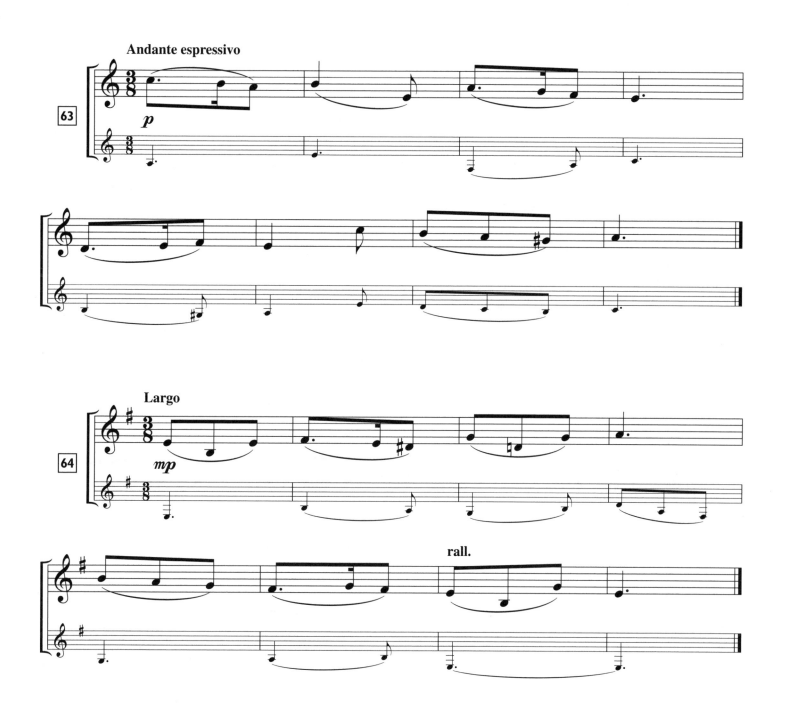

Putting it Together 8

The $\frac{6}{8}$ Time Signature

The time signatures dealt with so far i.e. $\frac{2}{4}$, $\frac{3}{4}$, $\frac{3}{8}$ and $\frac{4}{4}$ are called **Simple Time Signatures.** However, when main beats consist of dotted notes then the time is called **Compound**. The $\frac{6}{8}$ time signature indicates there are two dotted crotchet beats in the bar. Note however, a slow $\frac{6}{8}$ may be counted in six quaver beats.

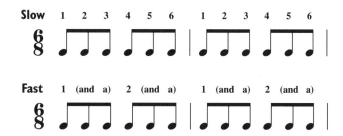

24

Grazioso

mp

p *cresc.*

mp

rit.

With sadness

mp

Lively, with spirit

Allegro

Swing Quavers

In Jazz music, quite often the quavers are said to be 'swung'. This means that the first quaver of every group of two on the beat is twice as long as the second (tripletised). Sometimes they are written as 'straight' quavers (♩♩♩♩) and sometimes as dotted quaver/semiquaver (♩. ♩♩. ♩), but there will always be an indication of the style from the tempo marking: e.g. 'swing feel'. Many composers now use the symbol (♫ = ♩³♪) to denote that any quavers in the music should be swung.

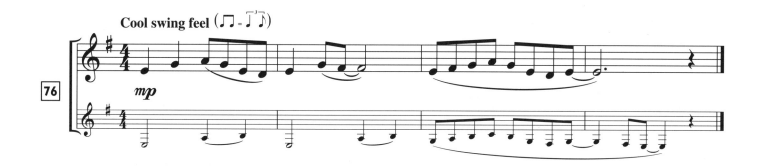

TOP TIP *In order to get into the correct 'feel', imagine that you are playing along with a jazz drummer.*

Putting it all Together with New Key Signatures

The following exercises include all of the elements covered in EYES AND EARS books 1 and 2. These are typical of the standard you would encounter in sight-reading tests in Grade 3 and 4 examinations.

 **TOP TIP** *Don't forget the key signature (if there are two sharps, they will always be F♯ and C♯.)*

Grade 3

 **TOP TIP** *(If there are two flats, they will always be B♭ and E♭.)*

Putting it all Together with New Key Signatures

Teacher's part

Grade 3

UE 21 142 L

31

Teacher's part

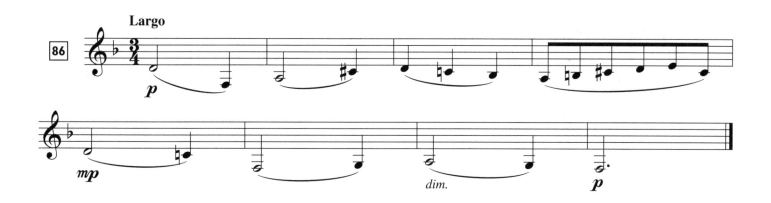

34

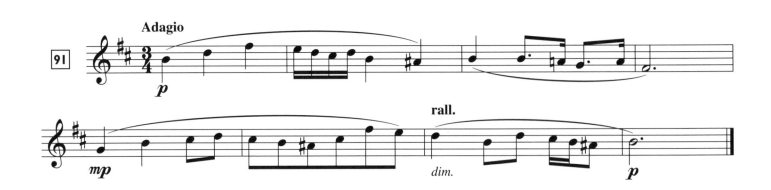

Teacher's part

Grade 4

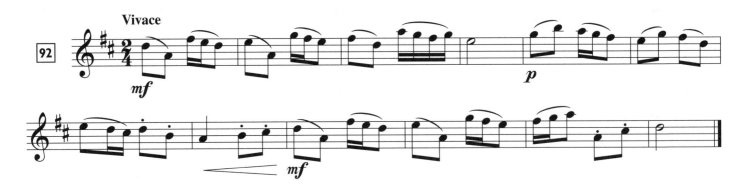

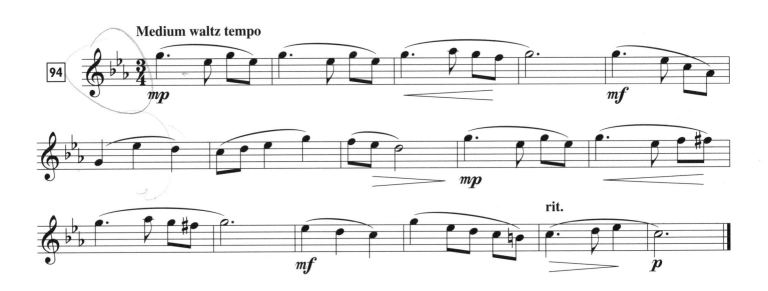

TOP TIP *If there are three flats, they will always be B♭, E♭ and A♭.*

Grade 4

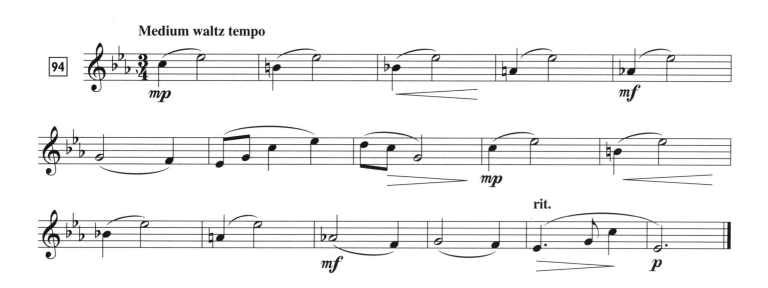

38

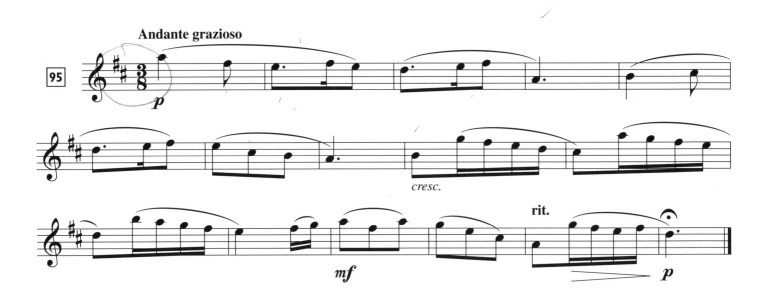

TOP TIP *If there are three sharps, they will always be F♯, C♯ and G♯.*

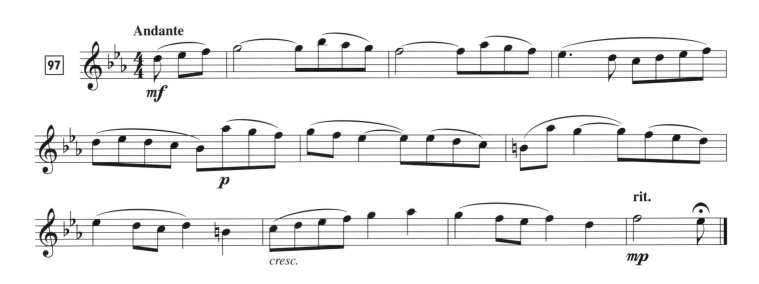

40

Teacher's part

British and American Terms

	BRITISH	AMERICAN	RESTS
o	semibreve	whole note	—
𝅗𝅥	minum	half-note	—
𝅘𝅥	crotchet	quarter-note	𝄽
𝅘𝅥𝅮	quaver	eighth-note	𝄾
𝅘𝅥𝅯	semiquaver	sixteenth-note	𝄿
𝅘𝅥𝅰	demisemiquaver	thirty-second-note	𝅀

bar　　=　　measure

A Glossary of Common Musical Terms

accelerando	getting gradually faster
adagio	very slowly
alla marcia	in the style of a march
allegretto	quite fast
allegro	fast
andante	at a moderate walking pace
cantabile	in a singing style
con moto	with movement
*crescendo (**cresc.**)*	getting gradually louder
*decrescendo (**decresc.**)*	getting gradually softer
*diminuendo (**dim.**)*	getting gradually softer
dolce	sweetly
doloroso	sorrowfully
espressivo	expressively
forte (f)	loud
fortissimo (ff)	very loud
giocoso	joyfully
grave	extremely slow
grazioso	gracefully
largo	broadly
lento	slowly
legato	smoothly
marcato	marked, accented
maestoso	with majesty
moderato	at a moderate speed
misterioso	mysteriously
*mezzo forte (**mf**)*	moderately loud
*mezzo piano (**mp**)*	moderately soft
*piano (**p**)*	softly
*pianissimo (**pp**)*	very softly
poco	a little
presto	very fast
*rallentando (**rall.**)*	getting gradually slower
ritardando (ritard.)	getting slower
*ritenuto (**rit.**)*	getting slower immediately
scherzando	playfully
staccato	short, detached
vivace	lively

Further Titles for the Clarinet

by James Rae

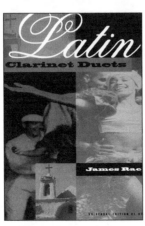

UE 19 735
40 MODERN STUDIES FOR SOLO CLARINET

UE 19 736
TAKE TEN FOR CLARINET

UE 19 764
BLUE CLARINET

UE 17 363
LATIN CLARINET

UE 21 073
LATIN CLARINET DUETS

UE 21 031
JAZZ ZONE – CLARINET *incl. CD*

UE 19 187
CHRISTMAS JAZZ FOR CLARINET

UE 21 103
GABRIEL FAURE – CLARINET ALBUM *Arr. Rae*

UE 16 593
**JAMES RAE'S JAZZ TRIOS FOR FLUTE,
CLARINET AND PIANO**

UE 16 594
**JAMES RAE'S JAZZ TRIOS FOR CLARINET,
SAXOPHONE AND PIANO**